100
Instrumental
Songs

Die schönsten und
bekanntesten Melodien
für Keyboard

100 Instrumental Songs
Die schönsten und bekanntesten Melodien für Klavier und Keyboard

Copyright © 2012 by Bosworth Music GmbH - The Music Sales Group

Songauswahl: Gerhard Hildner
Arrangement: Frank Speer
Layout: Musikverlag Monika Hildner
Covergestaltung: Julia Fahr

BOE7642
ISBN 978-3-86543-739-6

Printed in the EU.

www.bosworth.de

Buch DIN A4   100-023-4

www.musikverlag-hildner.de

100 Instrumental Songs

Musikverlag Monika Hildner
www.musikverlag-hildner.de

BOSWORTH EDITION
The **Music Sales** Group
www.bosworth.de

A Swingin' Safari

Swing ♩ 152

Music by Berthold Kaempfert
© 1962 by Tonika Musikverlag Kaempfert Schacht OHG, Hamburg.

Trumpet-Solo

D.S. al CODA

5

A Media Luz

| Tango | ♩ | 124 |

Adios Marquita Linda

Rumba | ♩ | 108

Music by Marcos Jimenez
© by Promotora Hispano Americana de Musica.
Für Deutschland: Peermusic (Germany) GmbH.

A Taste Of Honey

Shuffle ♩ 160

Music by Bobby Scott; Words by Ric Marlow
© 1960 und 1962 by Songfest Music Corp., New York. Für Deutschland, Österreich, Schweiz: MOOREA MUSIC Ulrike Schön eK.

A Walk In the Black Forest

Polka Beat   ♩   102

Amapola

8-Beat   ♩   177

Words & Music by Joseph M. Lacalle

Alohahe

Shuffle | ♩ | 103

14

Traditional

Amazing Grace

Slow Waltz ♩ 58

Another Suitcase In Another Hall

8-Beat | ♩ | 127

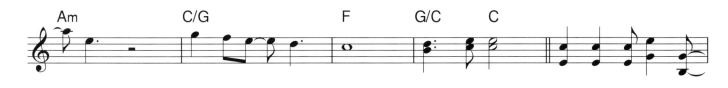

16

Music by Andrew Lloyd Webber; Lyrics by Tim Rice
© Copyright 1976 & 1977 Evita Music Limited.
All rights in Germany administered by Universal Music Publ. GmbH.
All Rights Reserved. International Copyright Secured.

Amboss Polka

Polka | ♩ | 100

Are You Lonesome Tonight

Slow Waltz ♩ 76

Words & Music by Roy Turk & Lou Handman

19

Aura Lee

Slow Beat ♩ 80

Traditional

Barcarole

Waltz	♩	148

Baby Elephant Walk

| 8-Beat | ♩ | 122 |

Music by Henry Mancini

(improvise ad lib.)

23

Besame Mucho

8-Beat | ♩ | 95

Blue Tango

Tango | ♩ | 118

Words by Mitchell Parish; Music by Leroy Anderson
© 1951, 1952 EMI MILLS MUSIC, INC.
Exclusive Worldwide Print Rights Administered by ALFRED MUSIC PUBLISHING CO., INC.

Biscaya

8-Beat | ♩ | 110

Music by Howard O'Melley, William Bookwood

Cast Your Fate To The Wind

Words and Music by Vince Guaraldi
© Claus Ogermann Prod. / Ebony.

Charmaine

Waltz | ♩ | 80

Chattanooga Choo Choo

Danny Boy

8-Beat   ♩   70

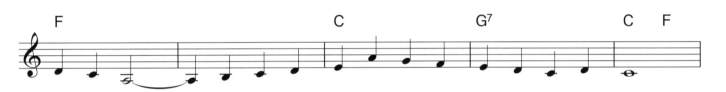

Traditional

31

Der dritte Mann (Harry Lime Theme)

| Polka Beat | ♩ | 176 |

Music by Anton Karas

33

Der rosarote Panther

Shuffle ♩ 116

(imrpovise ad lib.)

Dornenvögel

6/8 Beat | ♩ | 60

Dolannes Melodie

6/8 Beat   ♩.   55

Music by Paul de Senneville
© Editions Delphine / EMHA. Rechte für D/A: Rolf Budde Musikverlag GmbH, Berlin.

Early Bird

Disco Beat — ♩ 134

Music by André Brasseur

Edelweiß

Waltz ♩ 86

Einsamer Hirte

Slow Beat | ♩ | 64

Music by James Last

Ein Hauch von Zärtlichkeit

Foxtrot ♩ 84

Music by Henry Arland

El Condor Pasa

Slow Beat · 71

Traditional

El Cumbanchero

| Samba | ♩ | 152 |

Elisabeth-Serenade

Waltz ♩ 163

46

Music by Ronald Binge; Words by Christopher Hassall
© Copyright 1952 Ascherberg, Hopwood & Crew Limited.
Chappell Recorded Music Library.

Española cani

Flamenco Beat ♩ 120

Words and Music by Narro Marquina, Tallada Marquina

Eye Level
(Titelmelodie von „Van der Valk")

8-Beat | ♩ | 120

Fascination

Waltz   ♩   94

Music by Filippo Marchetti

Für Elise

| Waltz | ♩ | 90 |

Music by Ludwig van Beethoven

Games That Lovers Play

| Foxtrot | ♩ | 112 |

Music by Hans Last; Words by Larry Kusik, Eddie Snyder

Guitar Tango

Tango   ♩   127

Music by Francis de Goya

57

I Have A Dream

8-Beat | ♩ | 105

Words & Music by Benny Andersson & Björn Ulvaeus

If I Only Had Time

Slow Beat ♩ 80

Music by Michel Fugain
© by EDITIONS MUSICALES EDDIE BARCLAY.
Für Deutschland: Edition Marbot GmbH.

If You Could Read My Mind

In The Mood

Swing | ♩ | 148

(Sax Solo)

Il Silenzio

| Slow Beat | ♩ | 65 |

Java

8-Beat | ♩ | 170

Words & Music by Freddy Friday, Allen Toussant, Alvin Tyler
© Tideland Music Publishing Corporation. SV: AME Musikverlag Edward Kassner GmbH.

Kolokoltschik

Foxtrot ♩ 104

Traditional

Le Rêve

Waltz ♩ 84

Music by Traditional Arrangements by Roland Heck, Gerd Koethe, Hans Lingenfelder

67

Love's Theme

Foxtrot ♩ 98

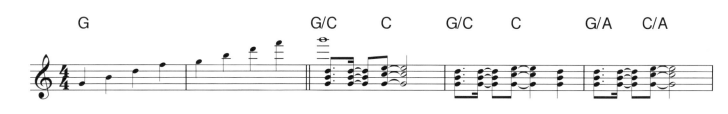

Love Story

Slow Fox   ♩ = 78

Words and Music by Francis Lai
© Copyright 1970 Famous Music Corporation.
All Rights Reserved. International Copyright Secured.

Mexican Whistler

6/8 Beat   ♩.   82

Mambo No. 5

| Mambo | ♩ | 174 |

Music by Perez ,Prez' Prado

Mexico

Fast Beat | ♩ | 216

Midnight In Moscow

Slow Fox | ♩ | 108

Music by Wassili Solowjew-Sedoj, Words by Michail Matusowski
© Mit freundlicher Genehmigung Musikverlag Hans Sikorski GmbH & Co. KG, Hamburg.

Moliendo Café

Latin Beat ♩ 174

Words and Music by Jose Manzo
© by Peermusic III Ltd.
Für Deutschland: Peermusic (Germany) GmbH.

Moonlight Serenade

Slow Swing ♩ 74

Music by Glenn Miller Text: Mitchell Parish

Morgens um 7 ist die Welt noch in Ordnung

6/8 Beat | ♩ | 64

78

Music by James Last
© 1968 Happy Musikverlag GmbH & Co KG.
Warner/Chappell Overseas Holdings Ltd, London.
Reproduced by permission of Faber Music Ltd. All Rights Reserved.

Morning Has Broken

Waltz ♩ 140

Music Box Dancer

Disco Beat   ♩   134

Music by Frank Mills

No More Boleros

8-Beat /Bolero ♩ 81

On Top Of Old Smokey

Waltz | ♩ | 170

Once Upon A Time In The West

Disco Fox | ♩ | 86

Patricia

Latin Beat | ♩ | 154

Pelican Dance

Disco Rock | ♩ | 86

Music by Bernard Estardy
© 2005 by Editions Musical Es Sforzando.
Rechte für Deutschland, Österreich, Schweiz: EMI Production Music GmbH.

Petite Fleur

| Ballad | ♩ | 80 |

Music by Sidney Bechet, Words by Sidney Bechet, Fernand Bonifay
© 1952 by Carroussel Editions Musicales – für D, A Harrison Musikverlag

Penny Lane

Pop Beat | ♩ | 120

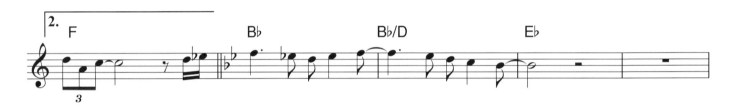

Pfeif drauf

Polka Beat ♩ 101

Music by Hans Jürgen Buchner

Puttin' On The Ritz

Disco Beat | ♩ | 98

Quartermaster's Store

Disco Rock ♩ 160

Raunchy

Pop Rock | ♩ | 142

Recuerdos de la Alhambra

Waltz ♩ 80

Red River Rock

Rock'n'Roll ♩ 154

Red Roses For You

Shuffle ♩ 104

Music by Günther Behrle
© Flamingo Music.

River Quai Marsch

Marsch | ♩ | 106

Music by Malcolm Arnold
© 1957 Shapiro Bernstein & Co Inc Film.
Shapiro Bernstein & Co Limited, New York, USA.
Reproduced by permission of Faber Music Ltd. All Rights Reserved.

Rondo Veneziano

| 8-Beat | ♩ | 130 |

Music by Gian Piero Reverberi & Laura Giordano

Sail Along Silvery Moon

Shuffle | ♩ | 90

Music by Percy Wenrich, Words by Harry Tobias
© Anne Rachel Music Corp.
Rechte für Deutschland, Österreich, Schweiz: EMI Music Publishing Germany GmbH.

Samba Pa Ti

| Samba Beat | ♩ | 86 |

Sentimental Journey

Shuffle | ♩ | 73

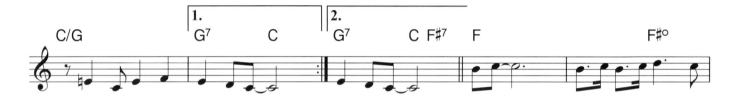

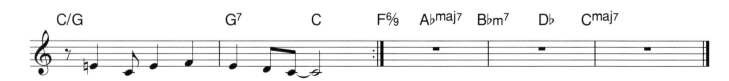

Silberfäden

Foxtrot | ♩ | 124

Music by Danks (traditional), Arrangement by Bob Wesling
© Edition Roland Musikverlag.

105

Slow Motion

Slow Shuffle ♩ 72

Music by Peter Drischel

Somewhere My Love

Waltz ♩ 174

Music by Maurice Jarre; Lyrics by Paul Francis Webster

Song For Guy

| 8-Beat | ♩ | 62 |

Words and Music by Elton John, Bernie Taupin

Song Sung Blue

Shuffle ♩ 120

Stranger On The Shore

Slow Fox | ♩ | 88

Music by Acker Bilk
© Sherwin Music Company, London/
Robert Mellin Musikverlag KG. Mit freundlicher Genehmigung der Bosworth Musik GmbH.

Tara's Theme

8-Beat	♩	114

Musik by Max Steiner

111

Tea For Two

Cha-Cha-Cha   ♩   119

Music by Vincent Youmans; Words by Irving Caesar
© 1924 Harms, Incorporated. Rechte für D/A: Rolf Budde Musikverlag GmbH / Rondo-Verlag GmbH.

Tequila

Latin Beat ♩ 180

The Entertainer

Polka Beat ♩ 140

Music by Scott Joplin

The Floral Dance

Polka Beat | ♩ | 182

Words and Music by Katie Moss
© 1911 Chappell Music Ltd, London.
Reproduced by permission of Faber Music Ltd. All Rights Reserved.

The Long Road

| Slow Beat | ♩ | 92 |

The Man With The Harmonica

Theme From „Elvira Madigan"

Slow Beat ♩ = 66

Music by Wolfgang Amadeus Mozart, Arranged by James Last

Theme From „A Summer Place"

6/8 Beat | ♩. | 60

Verde

Slow Swing ♩ 78

Music by Guido de Angelis, Maurizio de Angelis

Walzer Nr. 2

| Waltz | ♩ | 186 |

Wenn der weiße Flieder wieder blüht

Disco Fox ♩ 164

Wheels

| Rumba | ♩ | 128 |

Music by Norman Petty
© Dundee Music
Rechte für Deutschland, Österreich, Schweiz: EMI Music Publishing Germany GmbH.

Wilde Rosen

Waltz ♩ 74

Music by Gerd Koethe, Roland Heck, H Norden

Winnetou-Melodie

8-Beat · ♩ 82

Music by Martin Böttcher
© 1964 by SMV Schacht Musikverlage GmbH & Co. KG.

Wolkenreise

Disco Beat ♩ 114

Music by Eric Eroc

Wunderland bei Nacht

Slow Shuffle | ♩ | 71

Music by Klaus Günter Neumann, Willi Stanke

Zorba's Dance

Syrtaki / Polka   ♩   90/170

(langsam schneller werden)

(schneller werden)

Sie sind von diesem Buch begeistert?

Wir haben noch viele weitere tolle Liederbücher, Midifiles, CDs und Playbacks in unserem Angebot!

Interessiert?

Dann fordern Sie unseren kostenlosen Katalog mit allen Buchtiteln und Inhaltsangaben bei unten stehender Anschrift an!

Es lohnt sich!

100-023-4   Buch DIN A4   BOE7642
             Midifiles auf Anfrage   ISBN 978-3-86543-739-6

Musikverlag Monika Hildner
www.musikverlag-hildner.de

BOSWORTH Edition
The **Music** Sales Group
www.bosworth.de

Weitere Hits aus dem Bosworth-Verlag:

Hans-Günter Heumann
More Keyboard Kultsongs

BOE 7533
ISBN: 978-3-86543-600-9
19,95 €

Hans-Günter Heumann
Keyboard Kultbuch

BOE 7260
ISBN: 978-3-86543-106-6
19,95 €

Der Alleinunterhalter

BOE 6261
ISBN: 978-3-86543-651-1
26,95 €

Hit Session Country

BOE 7297
ISBN: 978-3-86543-146-2
21,50 €

Hit Session 3

BOE 7163
ISBN: 978-3-93704-174-2
20,50 €

Die Hitbox

BOE 7178
ISBN: 978-3-86543-429-6
14,95 €

BOSWORTH Edition
The Music Sales Group
www.bosworth.de